AGENT HANDBOOK

WORLD WAR TWO

D0410143

LIGHTNING QUIZ

The Second World War was one of the biggest conflicts in history.

It stretched across the world and lasted for many years. But how did it start? What was life really like? How did people feel?

This handbook will help you travel back to that time, but first, let's see how much you already know with this lightning quiz. Don't worry if you don't know the answers – you can find out everything you need to know in this book!

Use a pencil to fill in your answers, then you can do the quiz again or test a friend! Score one point for each correct answer.

1. **What year did the Second World War begin?**

   a) 1937 ☐
   b) 1936 ☐
   c) 1938 ☐
   d) 1939 ☐

2. **Who was the German leader during the Second World War?**

   a) Joseph Stalin ☐
   b) Adolf Hitler ☐
   c) Benito Mussolini ☐
   d) F. D. Roosevelt ☐

3. **During the war, food was so expensive that only rich people could eat well.**

   true ☐   false ☐

4. **Which of these is NOT a type of plane from WW2?**

   a) Spitfire ☐
   b) Hurricane ☐
   c) Lancaster ☐
   d) Jumbo jet ☐

5. At night, you could be fined if you lit a match in the street.

true ☐   false ☐

6. What was the name given to Britain, Russia, the US and other countries fighting against Germany?

a) The Friends ☐
b) The Allies ☐
c) The Chums ☐
d) The Pals ☐

7. What was the name of Britain's prime minister during the Second World War?

a) Tony Blair ☐
b) Theresa May ☐
c) Winston Churchill ☐
d) Margaret Thatcher ☐

8. The bombing of British cities was called:

a) The Blitz ☐
b) The Beast ☐
c) The Raid ☐
d) The Storm ☐

9. In London, some families sheltered from the bombing by sleeping in Underground stations.

true ☐   false ☐

10. Thousands of children were sent away from their families to live with strangers in the countryside.

true ☐   false ☐

HOW DID YOU SCORE?

7–10 – What a spiffing start! You really know your onions!

4–6 – Jolly good show! Your knowledge just needs a bit of polishing up!

0–3 – Chin up, old bean! Get swotting and you'll soon be a whizz at this war malarkey.

NOW TURN TO PAGE 76 TO CHECK ALL YOUR ANSWERS.

THE WORLD AT WAR

In 1918, after the First World War, Germany had agreed to give up land, money and much of its army. The following years were very tough. In 1933, the Germans voted for Adolf Hitler, leader of the Nazi party, because he promised to make Germany powerful again. But he got rid of anyone who disagreed with him and became the Führer (leader). Hitler was going to invade other countries to build a huge Nazi Empire. The journey to the Second World War had begun...

3 September – Britain and France (the Allies) declare war on Germany.

January – rationing begins (page 54).

1939 > > > > **1940** > > >

1 September – Hitler invades Poland. Britain evacuates children from cities (page 40).

April – Germany invades Norway and Denmark.

ADOLF HITLER >

May – Germany invades Belgium, France, Luxembourg and the Netherlands.
Winston Churchill becomes British Prime Minister.
Allied troops are rescued from the beaches at Dunkirk (page 32).

WINSTON CHURCHILL

June – Italy joins the war on Germany's side (the Axis powers).

August – the Nazi siege of Leningrad begins. It lasts for 872 days.

June – the Axis powers invade the Soviet Union.

September – The Blitz begins (page 50).

July – The Battle of Britain starts (page 34).

1941

December – Japan attacks Pearl Harbour. The United States enters the war on the Allies' side.

Hitler said Jewish people, other races as well as disabled people were enemies of the Nazis. They suffered terribly because of this and millions of people were sent to concentration camps, where many died.

1942

June – success at the Battle of Midway helps the Allies in the fight for control of the Pacific Ocean.

July – Germany suffers defeats at Stalingrad, Russia, and El Alamein, North Africa.

JOSEPH STALIN >

February – Nazi defeat at Stalingrad.

September – the Allies invade Italy.

1943

May – German and Italian troops surrender in North Africa.

June – the Allies launch the D-Day landings in Normandy, France (page 38). The first German V1 rocket attack on London.

1944

May – German troops surrender to the Allies.

April – the Soviet army advances on Berlin, Germany. Hitler dies in his bunker.

August – the Resistance uprising, Paris is freed from the Nazis.

1945

8 May – Victory in Europe (VE Day).

August – the United States drops atomic bombs on Hiroshima and Nagasaki, causing destruction on a scale never seen before.

15 August – Japan surrenders – the war is over.

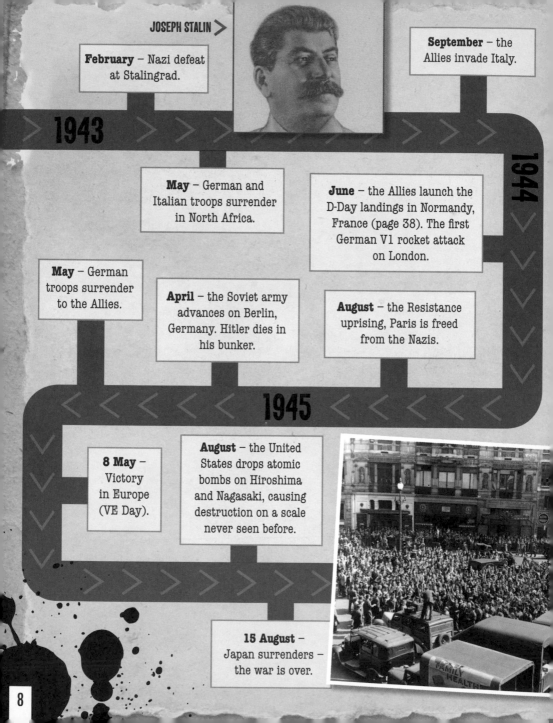

KEY PLAYERS

THE ALLIES

Winston **CHURCHILL** – British Prime Minister from 1940

Franklin D **ROOSEVELT** – US President until his death in April 1945

Joseph **STALIN** – leader of the Soviet Union

General Bernard **MONTGOMERY** – commanded Allies in the D-Day landings

General Dwight **EISENHOWER** – commanded US troops in Europe and Africa

General Georgi **ZHUKOV** – Russian commander who seized Berlin in 1945

THE AXIS POWERS

Adolf **HITLER** – Germany's dictator

Benito **MUSSOLINI** – Italy's dictator

Emperor **HIROHITO** – ruler of Japan

Erwin **ROMMEL** – Nazi General known as the 'Desert Fox'

Herman **GOERING** – Commander of the Luftwaffe (German airforce)

The words in bold are hidden in the grid below. Can you find them all?

M	S	E	I	S	E	N	H	O	W	E	R
U	C	X	G	O	E	R	I	N	G	T	H
S	H	A	R	V	B	W	Y	D	K	S	I
S	U	D	J	O	U	G	C	M	B	T	R
O	R	I	X	C	M	W	U	F	Q	A	O
L	C	W	L	V	O	M	P	Q	E	L	H
I	H	I	T	L	E	R	E	F	B	I	I
N	I	A	P	V	R	M	Q	L	T	N	T
I	L	D	S	Z	H	U	K	O	V	I	O
P	L	M	O	N	T	G	O	M	E	R	Y
R	O	O	S	E	V	E	L	T	X	A	U

A CALL TO ARMS

When the war started, some men volunteered to join the army, but Britain needed more troops.

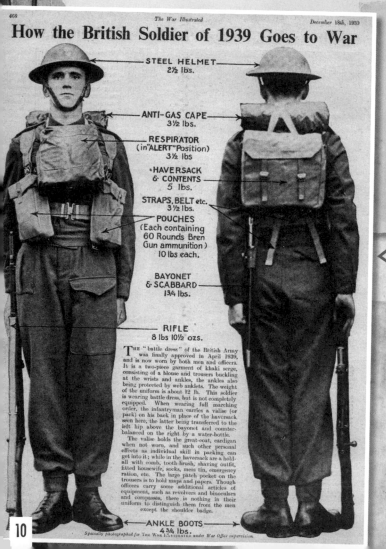

How the British Soldier of 1939 Goes to War

STEEL HELMET
2½ lbs.

ANTI-GAS CAPE
3½ lbs.

RESPIRATOR
(in "ALERT" Position)
3½ lbs

HAVERSACK
& CONTENTS
5 lbs.

STRAPS, BELT etc.
3½ lbs.

POUCHES
(Each containing
60 Rounds Bren
Gun ammunition)
10 lbs each.

BAYONET
& SCABBARD
1¾ lbs.

RIFLE
8 lbs 10½ ozs.

THE "battle dress" of the British Army was finally approved in April 1939, and is now worn by both men and officers. It is a two-piece garment of khaki serge, consisting of a blouse and trousers buckling at the wrists and ankles, the ankles also being protected by web anklets. The weight of the uniform is about 12 lb. This soldier is wearing battle dress, but is not completely equipped. When wearing full marching order, the infantryman carries a valise (or pack) on his back in place of the haversack seen here, the latter being transferred to the left hip above the bayonet and counter-balanced on the right by a water-bottle. The valise holds the great-coat, cardigan when not worn, and such other personal effects as individual skill in packing can get into it; while in the haversack are a hold-all with comb, tooth-brush, shaving outfit, fitted housewife, socks, mess tin, emergency ration, etc. The large patch pocket on the trousers is to hold maps and papers. Though officers carry some additional articles of equipment, such as revolvers and binoculars and compass, there is nothing in their uniform to distinguish them from the men except the shoulder badge.

ANKLE BOOTS
4¾ lbs.

Specially photographed for THE WAR ILLUSTRATED *under War Office supervision.*

10

New rules came in saying that men aged eighteen to forty-one could be conscripted or 'called up' to join the Army, Royal Navy or Royal Air Force (RAF). By the end of the war, more than 3.5 million men had served.

< NEWSPAPER PAGE SHOWING A TYPICAL BRITISH SOLDIER IN HIS WARTIME UNIFORM

RESERVED!

Some men worked in 'reserved occupations' such as teaching, mining and farming to keep the country running, so they weren't called up.

SPECIAL SKILLS

By 1943, the army tried to match up some conscripts' skills to the right army role. Where do you think you would belong? Take this quiz to find out!

1. How would your friends describe you?

a) Strong, dependable and always good in a crisis
b) Logical and practical, you always have a solution to a problem
c) Quite laid back – you tend to go with the flow
d) A bit of a daredevil

2. Choose a weekend activity:

a) Scout camp – your six would be lost without you
b) Building a treehouse in your garden
c) I'll let my mates decide
d) A 5 km run followed by a muddy obstacle course

3. How good are you in an emergency?

a) I'll calm everyone down – people listen to me
b) I'll always find a solution to put things right
c) I can be relied on to do whatever you ask of me
d) I'm always calm – nothing fazes me!

4. Your class must design and build a bridge that holds a person's weight. Do you:

a) Take charge immediately, making lists and giving everyone jobs to do
b) Use your technical know-how to come up with a bridge design
c) Let others take charge – you are happy to pitch in and help wherever you can
d) Volunteer to do the scary bit – you'll test the bridge!

ARE YOU MOSTLY A, B, C OR D? TO FIND OUT WHICH ARMY JOB YOU'RE SUITED TO, TURN TO PAGE 76.

MY ARMY TRAINING DIARY

by Jack Harris

October 1940

Passed the army medical with 'A1 fit'. Ordered to report for duty in three days' time.

November 1940

At the barracks, marched to army stores to collect ID disc, uniform, rifle and a gas mask, then to the barbers where our hair was shaved to stubble. Goodbye civvy street, hello army life.

November 1940

No time to write. Every minute filled. Feel like a proper soldier though.

December 1940

Getting the hang of packing my kit bag. It's got everything from grenades to a gas mask and spare socks to soap. Not keen on the field rations, though...

MAKE A 24-HOUR RATION PACK

YOU WILL NEED:

- a small cardboard box (about A5 in size)
- a packet of instant porridge
- two packets of instant soup
- a small tin of tuna or corned beef
- five plain crackers
- two sweet biscuits
- two packs of chewing gum (four pieces in each)
- five boiled sweets
- two tea bags
- six sugar lumps
- a small bar of chocolate

COULD YOU EAT THIS EVERY DAY?

SAFETY FIRST!

Ask a grown up to open the tin and prepare the oatmeal and soup.

ONCE COMPLETE, STICK A PICTURE OF YOUR RATION PACK HERE!

10 January 1941

Dear Frank,

Getting the hang of military lingo now. You keep pestering me to explain how the army works, so I've cobbled this together with the help of the lads:

You wanted the low down on the army, so here goes:

I'm a **private** (no badges yet). Me and eleven other lads make up a **section**, kept in line by the **sergeant** (Sarge).

The section and three others make up a **platoon**, who answer to the **Lieutenant**.

Our platoon and one other make a **company** of 200 men led by the **Captain**.

His company and two others make up a **battalion** of 1,000 men headed up by the **Lieutenant Colonel**.

Three battalions make up a **regiment**, or brigade commanded by the **Colonel**.

Three brigades are part of the **division** of up to 16,000 men, controlled by the **Major General**.

Three divisions make up a **corps**, overseen by the **Lieutenant General** (top brass).

Two or more corps make a **field army** of 150,000 men, headed by the very top brass — the **Field Marshal**.

So as you can see, I'm just a very tiny cog in the war machine.

Be good for mother,

Jack.

PARADE PUZZLE

Attention! Organize the troops in the grid below so that each picture appears once in every row and column. Write the correct number or draw a picture in each empty square.

1.   2.   3.   4.

To see if your army is present and correct, go to page 76.

ROYAL AIR FORCE

Some men were called up to join the Royal Air Force (RAF). As well as learning to fly, rookie pilots had lessons in navigation, Morse code and aircraft identification. To make sure they had as many pilots as possible, some were sent abroad to the United States to train. Pilots from other nations such as Canada, Poland and New Zealand also flew with the RAF.

Those who didn't pass their flying course would be sent off to train as navigators and bomb aimers, while those that did earned their pilot's badge or "wings'.

THE SPITFIRE GIRLS

The Air Transport Auxiliary (ATA) delivered planes from factories to the RAF airfields. Although it was unusual at the time, some women became ATA pilots; trained to fly everything from Spitfires and Hurricanes to enormous Wellington bombers.

ALLIED WOMEN PILOTS OF THE AIR TRANSPORT AUXILIARY SERVICE

IWM

LINGO

Gen up on the lingo of a wizzo wartime pilot. Chocks away!

ACE
SOMEONE WHO HAD SHOT DOWN SEVERAL AIRCRAFT

ANGELS
ALTITUDE, SO 'ANGELS 10' MEANT FLYING AT 10,000 FEET

BLIGHTY
BRITAIN

BROLLY
PARACHUTE

BOUGHT IT
SHOT DOWN OR KILLED

CHOCKS AWAY
LET'S GET GOING

CLOBBER
FLYING GEAR WORN IN A BOMBER

DAISY CUTTER
A PERFECT LANDING

DICEY DO
A DANGEROUS SITUATION

DOG FIGHT
MID-AIR COMBAT

DRINK
A RIVER, SEA OR LAKE

GEN UP
STUDY IN DETAIL/A BRIEFING

GONG
MEDAL

HEDGE-HOPPING
FLYING VERY LOW

JOLLY GOOD SHOW
WELL DONE, EXCELLENT

PEEL OFF
BREAK FORMATION AND ATTACK

RHUBARB
MISSION IN CLOUDY CONDITIONS

SQUIRT
A BURST OF MACHINE GUN FIRE

TALLY HO!
SAID WHEN ABOUT TO ATTACK

WIZZO!
FIRST CLASS, VERY GOOD

17

PLANE SPOTTING

**Pilots had to have their wits about them in the air.
A moment's hesitation could be fatal, so being 'genned up'
on aircraft identification was a must!**

PUBLIC WARNING SIGN TO IDENTIFY
BRITISH AND GERMAN PLANES

This poster shows how similar the planes were, with only small differences in the shape of the wings, tail and engine positions. Luckily, although planes were painted with camouflage, they had markings to identify them.

SPITFIRE

RAF planes had circles called 'roundels' on the side of the plane and also on the underside of the wings. Luftwaffe planes had an iron cross and a Nazi swastika on the tail.

MESSERSCHMITT BF 109

AIR FORCE ACTIVITY

Using the plane below, design markings and camouflage,
then think of a name for your air force.

My air force is called: _____

THE NAVY

In 1939, the Royal Navy had the largest fleet in the world. The ships fought to ensure goods and food could be transported and troops could land and fight the Axis powers.

It was very dangerous work, often in very rough seas, with attacks by enemy ships and planes as well as the danger of being torpedoed by a lurking Nazi U-boat.

∧ ARK ROYAL
AIRCRAFT CARRIER

AIRCRAFT CARRIERS

Aircraft carriers allowed planes to be used out at sea. HMS *Ark Royal* could carry sixty Fairey Swordfish bi-planes, with space-saving folding wings. You had to be made of stern stuff to pilot one of these planes – they took off using a giant catapult!

MAKE A COMPASS

Out at sea, where there are no landmarks, it's easy to wander off course. The ship's navigator had many instruments to help, including a compass.

YOU WILL NEED:

- a bar magnet
- a large sewing needle
- a cork
- a bowl of water
- scissors, or a sharp knife
- a small piece of sticky tape

1. Ask an adult to cut a 5 to 10 mm thick disc from the end of the cork with scissors or a knife.

2. Stroke the needle fifty times with the 'N' end of the magnet. Move it in one direction only from the tail to the tip, lifting the bar between each stroke.

3. Place the magnetized needle on the cork and tape it in place.

4. Place the cork in the bowl of water, needle-side up.

5. As long as the dish is away from computers, tablets or phones, the cork will spin so the needle tip points north!

▲ NAVIGATING OFFICER PLOTS COURSE

SAFETY FIRST!

Ask an adult to help you cut the cork and magnetize the needle.

BENEATH THE WAVES

Submarines were cramped and unpleasant. The crew slept in bunks wedged in all over the submarine – even the engine room. But that was nothing compared to the danger of being hit by a torpedo or depth charge.

Ships and submarines sent messages using Morse code. Each letter of the alphabet has a different combination of dots and dashes called 'dits' and 'dahs'. The alphabet looks like this in Morse code:

A	·—		N	—·		1	·————		.	·—·—·—		=	—···—
B	—···		O	———		2	··———		,	——··——		+	·—·—·
C	—·—·		P	·——·		3	···——		?	··——··		-	—····—
D	—··		Q	——·—		4	····—		!	—·—·——		$	···—··—
E	·		R	·—·		5	·····		'	·————·		@	·——·—·
F	··—·		S	···		6	—····		"	·—··—·			
G	——·		T	—		7	——···		(	—·——·			
H	····		U	··—		8	———··		)	—·——·—			
I	··		V	···—		9	————·		&	·—···			
J	·———		W	·——		0	—————		:	———···			
K	—·—		X	—··—					;	—·—·—·			
L	·—··		Y	—·——					/	—··—·			
M	——		Z	——··					_	··——·—			

SOS	···—··—···	break	—··· —·—
new line	·—·—·	closing	—·—· ·—··
new page	·—·—··	shift to Wabun code	···———
new paragraph	—···——	end of contact	···
attention	—·—·—	understood	···—·
error	········	invitation for named station to transmit	—·—·—·
wait	·—···	invitation for any station to transmit	—·—

MASTERING MORSE CODE

Imagine you are the commander of a submarine. You receive this Morse code message. Use the key to decode it. '/' is a space between words.

Once you've read it, choose from one of three replies below and write it in Morse code.

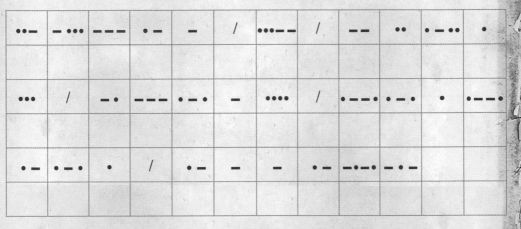

1. Torpedoes ready   2. Crew asleep   3. Leaving area

BEHIND ENEMY LINES

Secret agents were used by both sides during the war.
British agents were parachuted behind enemy lines to spy,
help the resistance and blow up trains and bridges.

Agents were picked for their cool, calm heads and their ability to blend in,
as well as their ability to fight. Many secret agents were women – if they
were seen carrying a shopping basket, few would suspect that there were
guns and explosives hidden under the food. They were the only women
to serve on the front line during the war.

SAFE OR COVER BLOWN?

Tick the boxes to say whether you think this would keep an agent
safe or blow their cover. Turn to page 77 for the answers.

	SAFE	COVER BLOWN
1) Wearing clothes made in England on a mission to France.	☐	☐
2) A convincing identity, with the right papers.	☐	☐
3) Knowing your cover story – and seemingly small details – inside out.	☐	☐
4) Being friendly and trusting everyone you meet.	☐	☐
5) Knowing how to change your appearance by cutting your hair, wearing it differently, adding glasses and so on.	☐	☐

CREATE A COVER STORY

Imagine you are a secret agent about to go on a mission. First, you need to fill in your identity card. You'll need a false name and date of birth, as well as a job for your cover story.

Next you need a photo (or a drawing of yourself) for your ID card. You might want to change your appearance slightly. Try combing your hair differently, adding a scarf, hat or glasses. Stick your photo in place.

Cover story: don't forget to rehearse your cover story. Details matter and a slip up could be fatal.

IDENTITY CARD

Name: ....

Profession: ....

Nationality: ....

Date of Birth: ....

DESCRIPTION

Height: ....

Hair Colour: ....

Eye Colour: ....

SECRET AGENT KIT

Secret agents carried ordinary objects that hid extraordinary things.

A hollowed-out pencil could hold a knife blade, a pipe might hide a compass and a simple matchbox might be a camera.

The most important bit of a secret agent's kit was their radio, hidden in a biscuit tin or suitcase. It was used to transmit messages about the enemy to their spy masters back home.

Draw your own piece of secret agent kit disguised as an everyday object. How could it be used and what would you call it?

SECRET AGENT INK

As well as hiding secret messages in pipes or shoes,
invisible ink could be used to hide a message in plain sight,
on a piece of paper such as a shopping list.

TO MAKE INVISIBLE INK YOU WILL NEED:

- lemon juice
- cotton buds or
  a thin paintbrush
- paper
- pencil

HOW TO:

1) Dip a cotton bud or paintbrush in the lemon
   juice and carefully write your message on the
   paper. You may want to use a code, too (see
   page 29) in case it falls into enemy hands.

2) Leave the paper to dry.

3) Once it is dry, use your pencil to write a
   shopping list on the paper so enemies think it's
   nothing of interest.

4) To read the message, you will need to gently
   heat the paper on a radiator, or by covering it
   with a cloth and asking an adult to carefully
   press it with a warm iron – make sure the
   steam function is off.

SAFETY FIRST!

Ask an adult to help you cut
the lemon and supervise if
you use an iron.

MAKE A NOTE OF YOUR SECRET MESSAGE HERE.

CODEBREAKERS

Both sides used coded messages during the war.

The Nazis had a powerful cypher machine, called Enigma, that they used to send messages. Messages were changed letter by letter by the machine to send it. To decode it, a second Enigma machine was needed, with the same settings. These changed every day and there were millions of combinations. So the code was thought to be unbreakable.

⋀ ENIGMA MACHINE

⟨ ALAN TURING

But the Allies had a secret team of codebreakers working at Bletchley Park, the British Code and Cypher School. Two of the team, Alan Turing and Gordon Welchman, built a machine called the Bombe. This, along with the Enigma machine found on U-boat 110, helped them to break the code.

By 1945, there were many Bombe machines and millions of Nazi messages had been decoded. The amazing work of the wartime codebreakers is thought to have shortened the war by about two years.

CRAFTY CODER

Use the grid below to create your own secret code.

You could use symbols, numbers or move letters a certain number of steps so that 'A' becomes 'D' and 'B' becomes 'E', for example. Use it to write messages to your friends or to write a secret diary.

A	B	C	D	E	F	G
H	I	J	K	L	M	N
O	P	Q	R	S	T	U
V	W	X	Y	Z	1	2
3	4	5	6	7	8	9

ANIMALS AT WAR

Extraordinary as it seems, many animals played an active part in the war. From carrier pigeons dodging enemy fire to carry important messages across the Channel, to dogs parachuting into enemy territory, or searching for people after air raids, there are some incredible stories.

Pigeon Power

Pigeons made some incredible flights during the war, carrying many life-saving messages. US Army Pigeon GI Joe flew 20 miles in twenty minutes. The message he carried saved the lives of more than 100 Allied troops who were about to be bombed by their own planes.

Bing the paradog

During the D-Day invasion, Bing, an Alsatian-Collie cross, parachuted into Normandy with British troops, where he was the 'eyes and ears' of the battalion, watching over them while they slept and alerting them to danger.

The Dickin Medal

The highest award a soldier can be given is the Victoria Cross. Animals have their own Victoria Cross, the PDSA Dickin medal. It was awarded to fifty-four animals who served in the Second World War, including Bing and GI Joe.

ROB THE COLLIE RECEIVING HIS DICKIN MEDAL IN 1945

YOUR HEROIC ANIMAL

Draw a picture of your favourite animal, or even your own pet.

What heroic deed would they have won a medal for?

DUNKIRK

The Nazis were using a new style of rapid fighting called 'Blitzkrieg' (lightning war).

Bombers attacked from the air, while tanks and troops smashed their way through ground defences. In just six weeks they invaded Belgium, the Netherlands and Luxembourg. France was next.

With the Nazi army moving across France, the Allies were pushed north where thousands of soldiers were stranded at Dunkirk. If they weren't rescued, the Allies would have to surrender.

So a daring evacuation mission began. Hundreds of vessels crossed the Channel to ferry the soldiers to safety, while RAF planes battled Nazi Stukas in the skies overhead. As well as Navy destroyers and minesweepers, there were many 'little ships' involved in the rescue from fishing boats and sailing yachts to lifeboats and barges, all crewed by brave volunteers.

DUNKIRK IN NUMBERS

Code name:	Operation Dynamo
Also known as:	The Miracle of Dunkirk
Soldiers rescued:	338,000
Time taken:	9 days from 27 May to 4 June 1940
Rescue vessels:	more than 900
Most soldiers rescued in a day:	68,014 on 31 May
Ships lost:	236
Smallest boat:	Tamzine, a 4.4 metre fishing boat

THE BATTLE OF BRITAIN BEGINS

After Dunkirk, Churchill made one of his most famous speeches, warning that Britain must be ready for the Nazis to invade:

"...we shall defend our island, whatever the cost may be. We shall fight on the beaches, we shall fight on the landing grounds, we shall fight in the fields and in the streets, we shall fight in the hills; we shall never surrender."

Write a stirring speech:

Imagine you are the prime minister in June 1940. Write an inspiring speech to encourage your country, while warning them that the road ahead will be difficult.

_____

_____

_____

_____

_____

_____

_____

_____

_____

THE BATTLE OF BRITAIN

In July 1940, the Nazis began bombing RAF airfields.

The plan was simple – without RAF planes to defend Britain, Hitler's troops could safely cross the Channel and invade. For the next two months, RAF Hurricanes and Spitfires took on the Luftwaffe's Messerschmitts in fierce dogfights above the south coast of England.

BATTLE OF BRITAIN IN NUMBERS

Code name for British Invasion: ....Operation Sealion

Planned invasion date:.............................15 September 1940

RAF planes: ....Supermarine Spitfire
....Hawker Hurricane

Luftwaffe planes: ....Messerschmitt Bf 109
....Messerschmitt Bf 110

Number of British planes (July 1940): 640

Number of Nazi planes (July 1940):...........2,600

Average age of RAF pilots:.........................20

Life expectancy of a Spitfire pilot: ....four weeks

Countries who flew with the RAF:.............15 (including Poland,
....Canada and New Zealand)

Radar at the ready

Britain used a new technology called radar to alert RAF crews that enemy aircraft were approaching.

Imagine you are a Spitfire pilot in the Battle of Britain.
You've been flying mission after mission, on very little sleep.
Take a moment to fill in your diary. How are you feeling?
What are your biggest fears?

_____

_____

_____

_____

_____

Now, imagine that you are a Luftwaffe pilot, flying missions
to Britain. How do you feel?

_____

_____

_____

_____

_____

_____

_____

By September, with the RAF still holding on, the Nazis changed tactics,
bombing cities at night. The Battle of Britain was over,
but the Blitz had begun... Find out more on page 50.

THE BATTLE OF THE ATLANTIC

Merchant ships brought much of the food and fuel Britain needed from other countries such as North America and Australia on slow, dangerous journeys across the Atlantic Ocean. This made them targets for attack.

Merchant ships travelled in groups called convoys, with warships to guard them from Nazi planes and U-boats. These German submarines stalked convoys in terrifying groups called 'wolf packs'. They would wait until night fell, silently surface in the darkness and launch an attack.

The Allies fought back with long-range planes, as well as better radar, which could be used on both planes and ships. They also had improved sonar for detecting U-boats. A further breakthrough was made on 9 May 1941, when HMS *Bulldog* captured U-110 off Greenland and sent men on board to see what they could find.

A BRITISH SHIP DEPLOYS A DEPTH CHARGE >

U-DECIDE

You and your crewmates from HMS *Bulldog* board the U-110, looking for anything that might help the Allies.

1. **Which part of the U-boat do you head for first?**
   a) The engine room
   b) The radio room
   c) The galley

2. **Time is limited, what do you decide to gather from the U-boat?**
   a) Maps and blueprints
   b) Paper with notes and messages
   c) The U-boat log
   d) Notebooks

3. **When you reach the radio room, you spot a strange machine and code books. They look out of place. Do you:**
   a) Leave them behind, it's probably nothing
   b) Take it and hand it to your captain straight away

4. **Next, you have to decide what to do with the submarine. Do you:**
   a) Tow it back to land so the Allies can study the U-boat
   b) Sink it, so the Germans think their secrets are at the bottom of the ocean

For the answers, go to page 77.

D-DAY

By June 1944, the Allies had gathered enough forces to try to fight back against the Nazis in mainland Europe. The attack wouldn't be easy – they would have to move quickly to capture landing sites, and then move thousands of troops ashore with tanks and other equipment.

ALLIED SOLDIERS DISEMBARK FROM TRANSPORT SHIPS

D-DAY INVASION OF NORMANDY

D-DAY IN NUMBERS

Code name:	Operation Overlord
Supreme Commander:	General Eisenhower
Leading the ground forces:	General Montgomery
Date:	6 June 1944
Naval vessels	7,000
Landing sites:	five beaches on the Normandy coast
Paratroopers:	18,000
Troops landed day one:	around 155,000
Troops landed by end of June:	845,000

TOP SECRET!

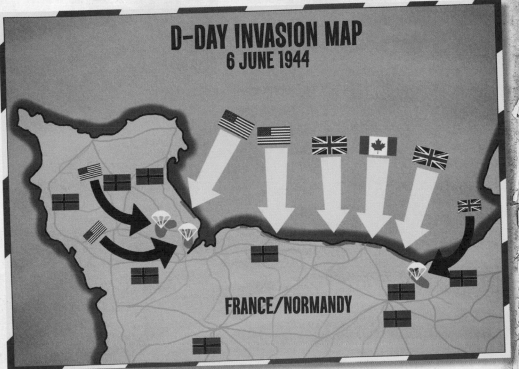

D-DAY INVASION MAP
6 JUNE 1944

FRANCE/NORMANDY

This message contains the codenames for the D-Day landing sites, but they've been scrambled in case they fall into enemy hands. Unscramble the letters, then once you've worked out each one label the map in the white arrows so that your troops can be briefed.

United States:	HATU	....
United States:	HMAAO	....
British:	LDGO	....
Canadians:	OUNJ	....
British:	RWDSO	....

THE HOME FRONT
EVACUEES

In Britain, at the start of September 1939, more than three million people were moved or 'evacuated' to the safety of the countryside from cities and towns that might be bombed.

Most evacuees were schoolchildren and their teachers, but mothers and children under five also went.

EVACUATION
IN NUMBERS

Code name:	Operation Pied Piper
Began:	1 September 1939
Officially ended:	March 1946
Numbers evacuated:	3,000,000
Also evacuated:	art and other national treasures, the Bank of England, some BBC productions

A LETTER HOME

Your family lives in Poplar, London, near the docks. Your entire school has been evacuated to Wales, where you and your best friend are staying on a farm. Write a letter home to your family to tell them about the journey and new experiences you've had.

WOMEN AT WORK

Before the war, women who married usually gave up their jobs to work within the home.

This all changed during the Second World War. With many working-age men away fighting, women had to step in and take on their jobs to keep the country running.

From December 1941, women aged between twenty and thirty were called up to work. They had the choice of joining the armed forces, the Women's Land Army or working in factories. At the height of the war more than seven million women were at work.

Women in the Land Army did back-breaking work on farms, while in the factories women made everything from planes and bombs to parachutes. In the armed forces, women operated searchlights and radar while others worked as codebreakers. A few even worked behind enemy lines as secret agents.

Put a tick by the activities that were done by women before the start of the war and a cross by those that were considered 'men's work'.

1. Driving a truck ☐
2. Flying a plane ☐
3. Cleaning the house ☐
4. Wearing trousers ☐
5. Doing the family food shop ☐

6. Working after they were married ☐
7. Doing plumbing ☐
8. Driving an ambulance ☐
9. Building ships ☐
10. Cooking dinner ☐

How many of these things do you think women were doing by 1944?

____ out of ten.

Even Queen Elizabeth II served in the forces – at the age of eighteen she joined the Auxiliary Territorial Service where she learned to drive and maintain army vehicles >

DAD'S ARMY

In May 1940, the call went out for volunteers to join the new Local Defence Guard.

In the first three months, nearly 1.5 million men who were too old, or medically unfit for the regular armed forces joined up to what became known as the 'Home Guard'. It was nicknamed 'Dad's Army' because most of the recruits were older men.

∧ KING GEORGE VI INSPECTING THE HOME GUARD

∧ BRITISH PRIME MINISTER WINSTON CHURCHILL INSPECTS THE LOCAL DEFENCE VOLUNTEERS

The Home Guard was the last line of defence if Hitler and his troops managed to invade. At first, uniforms and weapons were in short supply so they armed themselves with whatever came to hand – from golf clubs and broom handles to umbrellas. Over time, the Home Guard became a well-organized army, doing everything from manning anti-aircraft guns to patrolling streets.

IF THE INVADER COMES

As well as forming the Home Guard, Britain also did many other things to prepare for invasion. Can you work which of the following war preparations are true and which are false?

1. Road signs, station signs and milestones were painted over or removed.

    true ☐   false ☐

2. Church bells sounded every hour during the war years.

    true ☐   false ☐

3. A leaflet advised people to: 'think of yourself before your country'.

    true ☐   false ☐

4. Tank barriers, ditches and obstacles were built.

    true ☐   false ☐

5. The government warned people not to form a resistance army.

    true ☐   false ☐

6. Beaches were protected by mines and barbed wire.

    true ☐   false ☐

7. People were ordered to evacuate if the enemy invaded.

    true ☐   false ☐

8. In case of invasion, plans were made to destroy anything useful to the enemy, such as petrol pumps and trains.

    true ☐   false ☐

PUT THAT LIGHT OUT!

At night, enemy planes could use the light from houses and street lights to find and bomb cities and other important sites, so a blackout was introduced.

People had to cover their windows with heavy material, paper or paint. Street lights were switched off, lights on buses dimmed and car headlights covered so that only a tiny crack of light remained. The rules were so strict that even striking a match in the street was forbidden.

∨ BLACKOUT SHIELDS WERE FITTED TO THE HEADLAMPS OF CARS

BLACKOUT TIME TO-NIGHT IS AT

∧ AN AIR RAID WARDEN SETTING BLACKOUT TIME

The streets were patrolled by Air Raid Precaution (ARP) Wardens, who later became known as the Civil Guard. If they noticed a hint of light shining from a window, they'd shout, "Put that light out!"

MAKE A BLACKOUT TORCH

Although kerbs had white stripes painted on them, it was easy to get lost in the dark, even on familiar streets. People were allowed to carry torches, but the beam had to be covered by two layers of tissue paper.

TO MAKE YOUR OWN BLACKOUT TORCH YOU WILL NEED:

- a working torch
- tissue paper (about A4 in size)
- a ruler and pencil
- scissors
- a strong elastic band

SAFETY FIRST!

Ask an adult to help you cut the tissue paper.

HOW TO:

1. Fold the tissue paper in half.

2. Measure the diameter of your torch at the bulb end.

3. Starting at the corner of the tissue paper, draw a square that is at least 4 cm wider and taller than the torch diameter.

4. Cut out the square.

5. Place the square over the end of the torch, then put the elastic band over the paper to hold it in place.

Do you think you could find your way home during a blackout?

Stick a picture of
your torch here!

AIR RAID PRECAUTIONS

By the time war began, Britain had already started to prepare for air raids.

People were given gas masks, which they had to carry at all times. Public air raid shelters were built and the wail of the air raid siren soon became a familiar sound.

More than 1.5 million people volunteered as ARP Wardens. Each warden was responsible for an area called a sector. As well as their nightly blackout patrols, ARP wardens were in charge of public air raid shelters and, if an area was bombed, they would check the damage and speak to the emergency services.

⌃ TUBE STATION ACTING AS AN AIR RAID SHELTER

⌃ GAS MASK DRILL AT SCHOOL

ARP FIRST AID

ARP Wardens were also trained in basic first aid. Brush up on your first aid skills by learning how to make a sling for someone with an arm injury.

YOU WILL NEED:

- a triangular bandage
- a friend to bandage
- a chair for your 'patient'

HOW TO:

1. Ask your friend to sit on the chair holding their 'injured' arm bent at the elbow, using their uninjured arm to support it.

2. Slip the bandage behind their injured arm so that the long straight edge is draped over the opposite shoulder and runs vertically past their tips of their fingers down towards the ground. The short point should be brought out to the side, past the elbow of their injured arm.

3. Stand to the side of your friend, next to their injured arm. Take the end of the bandage draped over the shoulder and gently pull it around the back of their neck. Keep hold of the end and take the opposite end of the bandage in the other hand. Bring it up over the front of the injured arm so the two ends meet at the shoulder. Tie them in a knot.

4. Check that the bandage covers the entire arm to the top of their little finger.

5. Take the short point of the bandage and bring it up so that it covers the elbow. Twist the end several times to secure it, and tuck the end in.

6. Swap over and let your friend bandage you.

THE BLITZ

In September 1940, Hitler decided to try and make Britain surrender by bombing towns and cities to destroy ports, dockyards and factories.

When the air raid sirens wailed in the late afternoon of 7 September 1940, a thousand planes headed to London from Germany in an attack that became known as 'Black Saturday'. It was the start of the Blitz, which lasted until May 1941.

During the Blitz, London was bombed for more than fifty-seven nights in a row. The Nazis also bombed cities around Britain.

Over the course of the war, the Allies also bombed many German cities, including Cologne, Hamburg and Dresden.

BURNT OUT BUILDINGS DURING THE 'BLITZ'

THE BLITZ IN NUMBERS

began:	7 September 1940
bombs dropped over London (tons):	18,000
civilians killed:	43,500
civilians injured:	51,000
people made homeless:	2,250,000
longest continual bombing:	57 nights
other cities hit:	Belfast, Birmingham, Bristol, Cardiff, Coventry, Glasgow, Hull, Leeds, Liverpool, Manchester, Portsmouth, Sheffield, Southampton.

PICTURE MYSTERY

During the war, these were familiar objects. Can you guess what they were for? Draw lines to match the photo to the right description.

BABY GAS MASK

This was used to protect babies if there was a gas attack. It completely covered them so air had to be hand-pumped into the mask.

BARRAGE BALLOON

These were attached to metal cables and flown in the air to force enemy aircraft higher and make it harder for them to drop bombs.

SEARCHLIGHT

These powerful beams would light up enemy aircraft for anti-aircraft guns to shoot down.

STIRRUP PUMP

Used to fight small fires – one person would direct the hose onto the flames while the other pumped the water from a bucket.

AIR RAID SIREN

Nicknamed 'Moaning Minnies', their wailing noise warned an air raid was starting.

TAKE SHELTER

When the war started, thousands of Anderson shelters were delivered to homes around the country.

The shelters were made of corrugated steel and designed to be built in a pit about 1 m deep and covered with earth to provide extra protection.

Anderson shelters could sleep up to six people, but the metal boosted the sound of the bombs exploding and in winter they were freezing cold, damp and some flooded. Some families chose to have a Morrison shelter instead – this indoor shelter was a metal dining table that families could crawl under during air raids. Both types of shelter saved many lives.

In London, people who didn't have shelters at home took to sleeping in Underground stations and the caves at Chislehurst, while others made use of cellars, railway arches and even church crypts.

⋀ A FAMILY SEEKS REFUGE INISDE
AN ANDERSON AIR RAID SHELTER

⋀ AIR RAID SHELTER IN CENTRAL LONDON

PUBLIC AIR RAID SHELTERS
← 400

DESIGN AN AIR RAID SHELTER

Use this space to design an air raid shelter. Think about how many people it will hold, whether it is an indoor or outdoor shelter and what people might need inside. You could add benches, or bunks, and room to store food and drink.

Name of my shelter: _____

FOOD RATIONING

With food in short supply, the Government had to find a way to make sure that what they did have was shared out fairly.

In January 1940, bacon, butter and sugar became the first food to be rationed. By 1942, most foods were rationed and others were hard to find.

People were given ration books and had to register with their local shops, where the shopkeepers marked every purchase in their ration book.

↑ QUEUES FOR FOOD-RATIONING

This was a typical weekly ration for an adult:

- 50 g (2 oz) butter
- 100 g (4 oz) cooking fat/lard
- 225 g (8 oz) sugar
- 50 g (2 oz) cheese
- meat to the value of 1 shilling and six pence – about 450 g (1 lb) to 350 g (12 oz)
- 1 fresh egg
- 100 g (4 oz) bacon or ham
- 100 g (4 oz) margarine
- 1,200 ml (2 pints) milk
- 50 g (2 oz) tea

plus:
- 16 points per month to 'spend' on whatever they wanted such as tinned food, dried fruit and cereals
- 1 packet of 12 dried eggs every four weeks
- 350 g (12 oz) sweets every four weeks
- 450 g (1 lb) jam every two months

MEALTIME MATHS

Here is your ration book – fill in your name and address on the front.
Including you, there are three 'adults' in your wartime household.
Work out how much of the following items you can buy every week.

MINISTRY **MF** OF FOOD

RATION BOOK
1944-45

Surname..

Other Names..

Address...
(as on Identity Card)

Date of birth (Day)............... (Month)............... (Year)...............

| | | | R.B.4 7 | JUNIOR |

TEA: _____ g   **MILK:** _____ l

BUTTER: _____ g   **SUGAR:** _____ g

BACON: _____ g   Answers on page **78**.

THRIFTY DISHES

During the war, people needed recipes and ideas to make food stretch as far as possible.

Cookery books and magazines printed ideas for some rather unusual concoctions, such as 'mock crab', which contained dried egg, salad cream, cheese, but no crab!

There were strict rules about dining out, too. Menus were limited to three courses and there was a maximum charge of five shillings. This meant that restaurants had to serve smaller portions or cheaper food to make a profit. Fortunately, fish and chips weren't rationed and this quickly became something that everyone enjoyed.

Free!

The Stork Wartime Cookery Book

Cut this out post today

There are NO FOOD PROBLEMS when you have this book!

BECAUSE some foods are rationed there's no need to go short of nourishment or to put up with dull and uninteresting meals. With the help of Stork and the new Stork Wartime Cookery Book you will find that meals are not only just as attractive as they were before, but just as nourishing. And using Stork for spreading as well as for cooking ensures that you get your full supply of the essential Sunshine Vitamins A and D. Get your copy of The Stork Wartime Cookery Book right away! Remember — it's FREE!

STORK MARGARINE

Wins your favour with its flavour

Wise eating in wartime

from the Ministry of Food's KITCHEN FRONT BROADCASTS 4D

CRAZY FOR CARROTS

Carrots became a staple food during the war.

They were nutritious, could be grown at home and were naturally sweet, so often they were used instead of sugar in recipes such as cakes so the family's precious sugar ration could be used for other things.

DOCTOR CARROT
the Children's best friend

VIT-A

To get people to eat more carrots, propaganda posters were made, which said they could help you to see in the blackout. Some shopkeepers even popped carrots on sticks and sold them as substitute ice lollies!

BAKE A WARTIME CARROT CAKE

TO MAKE YOUR OWN WARTIME CARROT CAKE YOU WILL NEED:

- 225 g (8 oz) self-raising flour
- 85 g (3 oz) margarine
- 85 g (3 oz) sugar
- 115 g (4 oz) carrot, finely grated
- 55 g (2 oz) sultanas or raisins
- a small jug of water
- 1 egg
- greaseproof paper
- baking tin

HOW TO:

1. Ask a grown-up to pre-heat the oven to 220°C or gas mark 7.

2. Sift the flour into the bowl.

3. Add the margarine and rub it into the flour until it looks like fine breadcrumbs.

4. Crack the egg into a separate bowl, then add it to the mixture, along with the grated carrot and sultanas or raisins.

SAFETY FIRST!

Ask an adult to help you grate the carrot and use the oven.

5. Use a wooden spoon to mix the ingredients together – the mixture will be dry so add a tablespoon of water at a time until it is sticky. Take care not to add too much, you don't want to waste precious rations!

6. Line the baking tin with the greaseproof paper.

7. Spoon the mixture into the tin and spread it evenly using a spatula.

8. Ask an adult to put the cake in the oven, bake until it is golden brown, which will usually take about 40 minutes.

STICK A PICTURE OF YOUR CAKE HERE!

MAKE-DO AND MEND

Like many things, clothing and shoes were in short supply during the war.

Fabric was needed for army uniforms, parachutes and other essentials, so people had to 'make do and mend'. From 1941, clothing was rationed. At first, people received sixty-six clothing coupons a year, but by the end of the war it was just twenty-four coupons.

Go through your wardrobe

Make-do and Mend

WOMEN'S VOLUNTARY SERVICE RUN CHILDREN'S CLOTHING EXCHANGE

Clothing growing children was a constant struggle for mothers, but many were handy with a needle and thread and also knew how to knit and crochet. People soon learned to make use of whatever they could find – when a Luftwaffe plane was downed, the pilot's silk parachute was salvaged and used to make knickers for every woman in one village!

CLOTHING COUPON CONUNDRUM

Ask your parent or guardian if you can hold a 'Make-do and Mend' clothes swap with some friends. Ask each person to bring along an outfit they've outgrown or they're bored with, and then have fun choosing something different without spending a penny!

STICK PICTURES OF YOUR
CLOTHES SWAP HERE.

STICK PICTURES OF YOUR
CLOTHES SWAP HERE.

STICK PICTURES OF YOUR
CLOTHES SWAP HERE.

STICK PICTURES OF YOUR
CLOTHES SWAP HERE.

CLOTHING BOOK 1945-46 JUNIOR CB 4/8

This book must not be used until the holder's name, full postal address and National Registration Number have been written below. Detach this book at once and keep it safely. It is your only means of buying clothing.

HOLDER'S NAME_____
(in BLOCK letters)

ADDRESS_____
(in BLOCK letters)

HOLDER'S NATIONAL REGISTRATION No.

IF FOUND please take this book to any Food Office or Police Station

FOOD OFFICE CODE No. L48J

THIS BOOK IS NUMBER JD 661545

HOLD Pages I—VIII in one hand and TEAR ALONG THIS LINE

DIG FOR VICTORY!

The 'Dig for Victory' campaign encouraged people to grow vegetables and fruit at home and in allotments created in public spaces.

Across the country, lawns, tennis courts and even golf courses disappeared to be replaced by neat rows of crops.

Leaflets were made giving step-by-step instructions on digging and planting seeds and people were also encouraged to keep chickens and pigs.

PLANT A
'DIG FOR VICTORY' WINDOWSILL

TO GROW YOUR OWN DIG FOR VICTORY PLANTS, YOU WILL NEED:

- old jam jars or glasses
- water
- a windowsill in a warm, sunny spot
- plant pots or a small window box
- potting compost
- scissors
- vegetables such as a romaine lettuce, a head of celery and spring onions

For romaine lettuce, spring onions and celery:

1. Ask an adult to chop a disc about 5 cm tall from the bottom of the lettuce, spring onions or celery.

2. Place the bottom in a jam jar or glass and add about 2 cm of water to it.

3. Place the jar on the windowsill and change the water every day.

4. When new shoots have sprouted, half-fill pots or a small trough with compost and add the plants. Cover the bases with compost, leaving the shoots above the surface.

5. Mist them with water from a plant spray gun when the soil feels dry and enjoy your free food!

STICK A PICTURE OF YOUR WINDOWSILL HERE!

POWERFUL POSTERS

Propaganda posters encouraged people to pull together to help the war effort, while others were used to give advice or tell people that the war would be won. Some posters even warned people to be careful about what they said and did in case enemy agents were listening. Here are some examples of WW2 propaganda posters:

DESIGN YOUR OWN PROPAGANDA POSTER

Think about the message you want to send out. Will your poster give information, ask people to help the war effort or try to cheer them up?

READ ALL ABOUT IT!

In the 1940s, news travelled slower than it does today. There was no Internet, smartphones or 24-hour television. In fact, television broadcasts, which were very new, stopped altogether during the war years.

Instead, people relied on the radio, newsreels at cinemas and newspapers to find out what was happening. Both the Allies and Axis powers loudly celebrated their successes while other less favourable stories were played down or not mentioned at all, to keep up morale. Some news stories that might be useful to the enemy were also kept quiet.

Radio broadcasts were also used in surprising ways. BBC European radio services broadcast secret coded messages to resistance fighters. The messages, such as 'the woman stroked the dog's nose' seemed meaningless even to the radio staff, who were never told their true meaning. But they would tell agents all sorts of things, such as when documents were received, a person was safe or to cancel a mission.

CHURCHILL ADDRESSES THE NATION >

NEWSFLASH!

This urgent piece of news has just landed on your desk at radio HQ. Write a brief radio announcement and record it, then broadcast it to your family.

August 1944

After four years of Nazi occupation, last night the French Second Armoured Division liberated Paris. The German commander of Paris, General Dietrich von Choltitz has signed a surrender agreement. French leader general Charles de Gaulle returned from exile to Paris earlier tonight and said in a broadcast that the French would not rest until the Nazis were defeated.

WRITE YOUR ANNOUNCEMENT HERE.

CREATE YOUR OWN WARTIME COMIC

War stories and heroes were really popular with children in comic books. Even so, rationing meant readers had to wait for each edition as comics such as the *Beano* and *Dandy* were published fortnightly rather than weekly to save paper and ink.

Create your own wartime comic strip story. Come up with a snappy title for your comic strip heroes, and then get drawing – the funnier the better!

The name of my comic is:

VE DAY

After almost six years of hardship, danger and destruction, the war came to a close in Europe when Hitler died and the Nazis surrendered.

'Victory in Europe' or 'VE' Day' was declared on 8 May 1945. Miles of bunting hung from the lamp posts and people put out tables and chairs for street parties.

In London, people gathered in Trafalgar Square, Piccadilly Circus and the Mall to celebrate the end of the war. But for others, the war continued and hostilities did not officially come to a close until September 1945.

VE DAY IN NUMBERS

Date of VE day: ....8 May 1945

Estimated crowd in Piccadilly Circus, London: 50,000

Clothes rationing ended: 1949

Food rationing ended: 1954

Final surrender documents signed,
Second World War officially ended: ....2 September 1945

Total duration of the Second World War: ....5 years, 364 days

CHURCHILL AND MEMBERS OF HIS CABINET WAVE TO CROWDS IN WHITEHALL

VE DAY – CELEBRATIONS IN TRAFALGAR SQUARE

MAKE YOUR OWN BUNTING

TO MAKE YOUR OWN CELEBRATION BUNTING, YOU WILL NEED:

- 2 m of string or wool
- 4 sheets of A5 paper (or two sheets of A4 paper folded along the short side and cut in half)
- a ruler

- a pencil
- scissors
- a glue stick
- colour pens, stickers and glitter to decorate your bunting

HOW TO:

1. Take one of the pieces of paper and use your ruler to measure a point approximately 7 cm from the corner of the long edge. Mark it with a small dot (2). On the opposite long edge, mark a point that is about 14 cm from the corner (3).

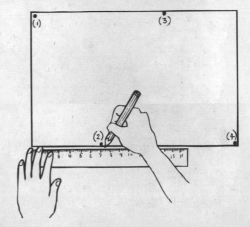

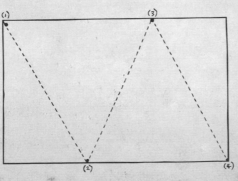

2. Using the ruler to draw a diagonal line from the bottom left corner, marked 1, to the dot at 2, then draw a second diagonal line to join 2 to 3. Finally draw a third diagonal line to join 3 to 4.

3. Carefully cut along the diagonal lines to make the first two bunting triangles.

4. Repeat steps 1 to 3 for the other pieces of paper.

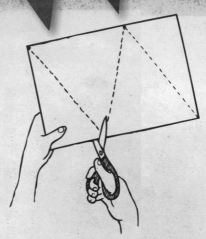

FOLD

GLU

5. Take a triangle and make a fold approximately 1.5 cm deep along the short edge, repeat for the other seven.

6. Decorate each triangle – use felt tip pens, stickers and glitter to make them look bright and cheery for your celebration.

7. Stretch out the string along the floor and place your triangles at regular intervals along the length – remember to leave some extra space at each end so your bunting can be fastened.

SAFETY FIRST!

Ask an adult to help you with the cutting out.

8. Once you are happy, turn the first triangle over and run the glue stick along the folded edge.

9. Hang the triangle over the string and press the fold down onto the back of the triangle, so the string is glued securely inside the fold.

10. Repeat this step for the rest of the triangles.

11. Hang up your bunting and get ready to celebrate!

VE DAY MEMORIES

The chances are that you might have a relative, family friend or neighbour who is old enough to remember VE day. Ask your parent to help you to interview them so you can hear a first-hand account of celebrations and what changed over the next few years.

Write down their stories and photocopy pictures, once you have enough turn it into your very own scrapbook.

HONOURING HEROES

Military decorations are medals that are given to people who have served in the armed forces.

Some, such as the **War Medal 1939–1945**, were awarded to everyone who took part – you may find that your family or a friend's family has one that belonged to your grandfather or great-grandfather if they served in the Second World War.

Those who showed exceptional bravery or courage were recognized with a special honour called an 'operational gallantry award', which includes the **Military Cross**, the **Distinguished Flying Cross** and the highest of all, the **Victoria Cross**.

∧ VICTORIA CROSS

∧ DISTINGUISHED FLYING CROSS

∧ WAR MEDAL 1939 – 1945

GEORGE CROSS

George Cross

Four female secret agents, Violette Szabo, Odette Sansom, Noor Inayat Khan and Nancy Wake were awarded the George Cross, the highest gallantry award for civilians, in recognition of their bravery behind enemy lines.

REMEMBRANCE

The Armistice that ended the First World War was signed on 11 November 1918. It agreed that fighting would end at the 'eleventh hour of the eleventh day of the eleventh month'.

THE CENOTAPH IS THE SITE OF THE ANNUAL NATIONAL SERVICE OF REMEMBRANCE

Since then, 11 November has become a day to honour those who died in all conflicts, including the Second World War.

It is usually marked with a two-minute silence at 11am to remember those who died. In Britain, parades are held on the second Sunday in November and poppy wreaths are laid at war memorials.

In the months after the First World War ended, people noticed that poppies had started to bloom across the battlefields. Since 1921, the poppy has been worn to remember those who gave their lives in the First World War and other conflicts since, including the Second World War.

ANSWERS

PAGES 4-5

1. d),
2. b),
3. false,
4. d),

5. true,
6. b),
7. c),
8. a),

9. true,
10. true,

PAGE 9

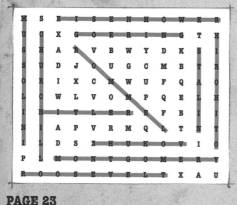

PAGE 11

mostly a) – you are a natural leader, you'd make an excellent army officer

mostly b) – you are practical and a problem-solver, you'd be a great engineer

mostly c) – you are reliable and a team player, you'd be perfect for the infantry

mostly d) – your daring nature and bravery means you'd be a true asset to special forces

PAGES 14-15

PAGE 23

••	– •••	– – –	•–	–	/	•••– –	/	– –	••	•–••	•
U	b	o	a	t	/	3	/	m	i	l	e

•••	/	–•	– – –	•–•	–	••••	/	•– – •	•–•	•	•– – •
s	/	n	o	r	t	h	/	p	r	e	p

•–	•–•	•	/	•–	–	–	–•–•	–•–			
a	r	e	/	a	t	t	a	c	k		

–	– – –	•–•	•– – •	•	– ••	– – –	•	•••	/	•–•	•
t	o	r	p	e	d	o	e	s	/	r	e

•–	– ••	–•– –									
a	d	y									

76

ANSWERS

PAGES 24-25

1) cover blown
2) safe
3) safe
4) cover blown
5) safe

PAGES 36-37

1. b) the radio room is a good place to start, you might find some messages to help the Allies.
2. All of them! There could be some really useful intelligence hidden in the paperwork.
3. If you answered b, well done! You've just made an important break through for the Allies. You've captured an Enigma machine and code books. Thanks to you, convoys will be safe from attack for weeks as the code breakers at Bletchley Park can crack the code!
4. b) You must sink the U-boat so the Nazis don't suspect you have the Enigma machine. If they keep using the same codes, you'll be able to read their U-boat messages.

PAGES 38-39

United States:.......**UTAH**   British: ....**GOLD**   British: ....**SWORD**

United States:.......**OMAHA**   Canadians: ....**JUNO**

PAGE 43

1. driving a truck ✗
2. flying a plane ✗
3. dusting the house ✓
4. wearing trousers ✗
5. doing the family food shop ✓
6. working after they were married ✗
7. doing plumbing ✗
8. driving an ambulance ✗
9. building ships ✗
10. cooking dinner ✓

By the end of the war, women were doing all these things.

ANSWERS

PAGE 45

1. true

2. false – they would only ring to warn of an invasion

3. false – it actually advised people to 'think always of your country before you think of yourself'

4. true

5. false – a secret resistance network was created and trained

6. true

7. false – people were asked to stay put and try to disrupt or slow down enemy troops

8. true

PAGE 51

BABY GAS MASK

This was used to protect babies if there was a gas attack. It completely covered them so air had to be hand-pumped into the mask.

BARRAGE BALLOON

These were attached to metal cables and flown in the air to force enemy aircraft higher and make it harder for them to drop bombs.

SEARCHLIGHT

These powerful beams would light up enemy aircraft for anti-aircraft guns to shoot down.

STIRRUP PUMP

Used to fight small fires – one person would direct the hose onto the flames while the other pumped the water from a bucket.

AIR RAID SIREN

Nicknamed 'Moaning Minnies', their wailing noise warned an air raid was starting.

PAGE 55

tea:	150 g (5 oz)
butter:	150 g (5 oz)
bacon:	300 g (11 oz)
milk:	3,300 ml (5 ½ pints)
sugar:	675 g (1 lb 8 oz)